LITTLE BOOKS ABOUT BIG STUFF

About God

A Unitarian Universalist
Book for Kids

Edited by: Betsy Williams, Jane Rzepka, Ken Sawyer and Noreen Kimball

Illustrated by Hannah Holby

Acknowledgements

This publication was made possible by a grant from the Unitarian Sunday School Society and support of the Church of the Larger Fellowship, Unitarian Universalist.

In this publication, when referring to God as an entity that people might or might not believe in, we treat it as a proper noun and capitalize it. When referring to god as a general concept, we treat it as a common noun and do not capitalize it.

A WORD OF INTRODUCTION FOR ADULTS

God is a challenging concept to talk about with young children. Many people have difficulty defining a concept of god and expressing their beliefs in adult terms, let alone in terms children can understand. For some of you, just hearing the word "god" conjures images and traditions you have intentionally rejected and don't want to revisit. For others, the word "god" has a foundational place in your personal theology. Whatever your beliefs, because children hear the word all around them, most parents and others who care for young children need to talk with kids about the idea of god. Children want to know if such a being or thing exists and what it means to them.

With this book, we hope to make this challenge easier for you. In "The Ferris Wheel," a group of Unitarian Universalist kids learn from each other that Unitarian Universalists may have different beliefs about God and that it's okay to be uncertain about one's beliefs. In the "Question and Answer" section that follows the story, we offer direct, honest, and concise answers to some of the questions children most commonly ask about God. As you might expect, many of the answers include some form of "no one really knows" or "people decide for themselves." It is important to convey this acceptance of diverse beliefs as a strength of Unitarian Universalism. As tempting as it is to provide our children with clear, unambiguous answers, they grow by feeling free to explore and confirm their own beliefs. (And so do we!) Finally, we offer three short vignettes of experiences some Unitarian Universalists would call experiences of God. We conclude each vignette with a question we hope will stimulate reflection and discussion.

Whether you use the word "god" to make meaning of the world around you or not, we hope this volume will help you explore it with the young children in your lives. — Betsy Williams

The Ferris Wheel

by Ken Sawyer

"Wow!" shouted Toby. "Look at the size of that Ferris wheel!"

"It's humongous!" Alyce exclaimed as the car pulled into the fairgrounds parking lot. She was sitting next to Toby in the back seat. Their friend Ryan was in front with his mom.

"I can't wait to go on it," Toby said.

But Ryan said, "I'm not so sure about that Ferris wheel. It is very, very tall."

Ryan's mom said, "Don't worry. Let's eat first. I'm hungry!"

"And then we can play games and win some prizes," added Ryan.

At lunch Ryan's mom asked what they had talked about that morning in Sunday school. Toby answered politely, "God."

"Really," said Ryan's mom. "Tell me more."

"Well," said Alyce, "it turns out people have all sorts of ideas about who God is, or who the gods are, or if God exists."

Toby added, "I think God exists."

"I don't," said Ryan.

"But that's okay," said Alyce, "like we were talking about in Sunday school this morning, people have different ideas about God in our religion. And some people aren't sure what they believe in."

"So true," said Ryan's mom.

After lunch the kids got a huge cotton candy to share for dessert. At the ring-toss, Ryan won a goofy toy clown.

Then they turned a corner, just past the fried dough stand, and there it was, straight ahead – the Ferris wheel! Its cars were painted bright purple and yellow, and each one was big enough to hold three people if they squeezed in tight.

"Wow!" shouted Toby and Alyce together.

Ryan didn't say so, but he had never been on a Ferris wheel and he was feeling nervous. Maybe even a little scared. Maybe even a lot scared.

But Alyce and Toby were eager, so Ryan followed as they all piled into a car and settled in for the ride. The car door clanked shut. The safety bar locked into place across their laps and they grabbed on. With a jolt the car started, carrying them up and up and up!

Ryan could feel his heart racing as the ground got farther and farther away. He started to sweat. His stomach didn't feel so good, and it wasn't just because he had eaten so much cotton candy.

Then Alyce started bouncing up and down and rocking from side to side, laughing as she made the car rattle and sway.

"Hey," said Ryan. "Cut it out!"

"Sorry," said Alyce. "You aren't scared, are you?"

"No way," said Ryan, biting his lip. "Not me."

Up and up the car climbed, until they were at the very top.

Suddenly the Ferris wheel lurched to a stop, and the car started swinging forward and back, forward and back. Ryan wished the swinging would stop, but there was nothing any of them could do.

Had something gone wrong? Were they stuck up there? How would they get back to the ground? Ryan didn't dare look down.

For a moment, they all stared ahead in silence, holding tight to the safety bar.

Finally Ryan said softly, "I think maybe now I am scared a little."

 "Don't worry, " said Toby. "I don't think anything bad's going to happen. The way I hear it, God looks out for people."

Ryan had heard other people say that, but it never made him feel any better.

Alyce asked, "What does God have to do with a Ferris wheel? God is the spirit of peace, justice, and love, good things like that. Ferris wheels are machines, made by people who know how to make them safe. They check them and fix them when they have to. Look," she said as she leaned over and looked down, "I can see repair people down there right now."

Ryan sure didn't feel like looking down, but hearing his friends talk made him feel better. And he remembered how taking deep breaths helped him in times like this. So he took a few really slow, deep breaths and started to feel stronger and calmer inside.

Alyce said, "I'm sure we'll be okay – but still, I'm glad you guys are here too. My mom says that's what God is, people sticking together."

"Well, it does help a lot that we're in this together," Ryan agreed. "But I wish we had something to do while we wait for them to —"

He hadn't even finished his sentence when the Ferris wheel started moving again. It went around smoothly three more times. Alyce was happy just to enjoy the view without rocking the car, Toby was happy to be up in the air, and even Ryan relaxed and enjoyed the ride.

Back on the ground, they were greeted by Ryan's mother. "I hope it wasn't scary up there when the wheel stopped so suddenly," she said. "I was worried."

"Yeah, it was sort of scary at first," Alyce admitted. "But I knew the repair people could fix it."

"I thought our whole car might fall off!" said Ryan. But he realized that after the scary part, the ride had been fun.

"I loved the whole thing," said Toby. "Are you guys ready for the roller coaster?"

"I am, for sure," said Alyce. "These are great rides!" She believed that people had designed them carefully and built them well.

"Me too, for sure," said Toby. "The higher the better!" He believed that God was looking out for him.

Ryan paused only a second before saying, "Me, too," and then, "for sure!" He believed that even if things got scary, he could get himself through, especially with friends by his side.

And off they ran.

Questions & Answers about God

by Jane Rzepka

What is God?

The word "god" can mean a whole lot of different things. When some people talk about God, they mean something like a person who knows and sees everything and who can make things happen. Other people think of God as an invisible power way bigger than us. Or God could be a feeling, like love, or fairness, or peace. When a person says the word "god," it might mean nature, or beauty, or everything good. There are places where people imagine God to be an antelope, or a mountain, or a bolt of lightning, or just about anything. God can even mean the whole universe! A lot of people believe in more than one god. And a lot of other people don't believe in any god at all.

Is God real?

Some people say yes, some say no, others aren't sure, and still others don't think about it much one way or the other. But no one knows.

Do I have to believe in a god?

No. There are good people everywhere who don't believe in any god, and good people everywhere who do. Unitarian Universalists believe that you are free to decide for yourself.

What does God look like?

If you are thinking of a god who is like a person, you might wonder how big this god is, what color God's skin is, if God has a long beard, or if God is a man or a woman or not exactly either one. You wish you could see a picture! Since no one knows what God looks like, you can draw your own picture. It may not look like the god your friends and relatives believe in, but that's OK!

Does God get angry?
Does God love me no matter what I do?

You can find stories about all kinds of gods—including loving gods and gods who get mad. But as you might have guessed by now, no one really knows! Many Unitarian Universalists believe in a god who helps us feel better when we're sad, who gives us energy for growing into healthy people, who wants the best for every person, and who is loving. Others don't believe in a god who has feelings.

Can God make stuff happen?

You may hear that God has special powers, like changing the weather for your picnic, sinking the basketball right into the basket, or making your grandmother get well. You may hear that it was God who started everything, God who made the world, God who makes lives better, God who causes people to die or suffer. Is it true? We have no way of knowing.

What Unitarian Universalists *do* know is that each one of us has power to work for the good. We can't control everything, that's for sure, and whether God can make stuff happen or not—we know *we* can!

Is God in charge of me? Is God watching me? Can I talk to God?

Some people believe that there's a god that pays attention to them and plans what will happen to them. Others don't think that makes sense.

Some people believe that you can talk to God and God hears you, others think that it's the talking that's important, and it doesn't matter if there's a god who hears you or not.

Do people ever change their mind about God?

Yes. Ideas about gods keep changing. Once, lots of people believed in a god named Zeus and now nobody does. That's what happens.

Unitarian Universalists believe that your own ideas are apt to grow and change during your life.

Whether you use the
word "god" or not,
what's important is that
you are a loving person
who makes the world
a better place.

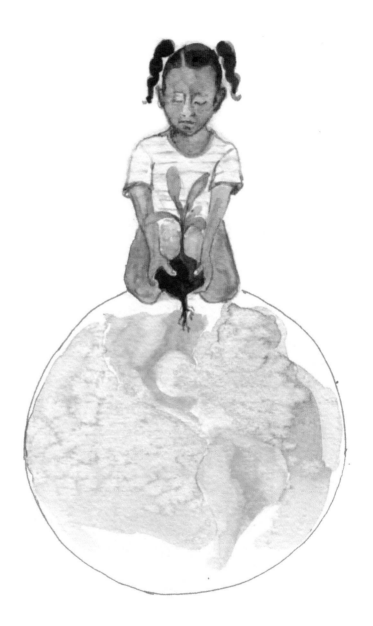

Would You Call That God?

by Betsy Hill Williams

Oneness of Everything

The sand was still warm from a day of hot sun. We snuggled in our sleeping bags and waited for night to come. We were far from town so we saw no lights in the distance. No airplanes above. No sounds. Just sand and sky. And then stars. Bright stars, dim stars, shooting stars. Thousands, millions, billions of stars! I felt like I was in outer space, part of the universe, floating among the stars.

Some people would call this vast, mysterious universe that we're all a part of, God. Some would not. Would you?

Love and Goodness

My family and I had just moved to the most awesome house on the beach when the hurricane hit. We had to get away as fast as we could. When we returned, I didn't even recognize our new home. The roof was gone and everything inside was ruined. Then an amazing thing happened. People from all over the United States—and I mean from as far away as you could possibly get—came to help us clean up. Total strangers helped us dig out the mud and sand and find what belongings we could. I even made a new friend, Lucas, who came with his whole family. I will never forget him, or the hundreds of other people who came to help.

Some people would call the spirit of love and the power of goodness, God. Some would not. Would you?

Nature

I was stuck at my Aunt Sandy's for the afternoon—no friends, no Internet, no TV. I was ready to be bored. I lay down in her worn-out old hammock. A spider scurried into view and began repairing a web that was hanging between two trees right next to me. I was hypnotized. I've done lots of arts and crafts, but I could never have made something as delicate and strong as that web. The afternoon went by and I didn't even notice. I was lost in the beautiful world that hung above my head.

Some people would call the beauty of nature, God. Some would not. Would you?

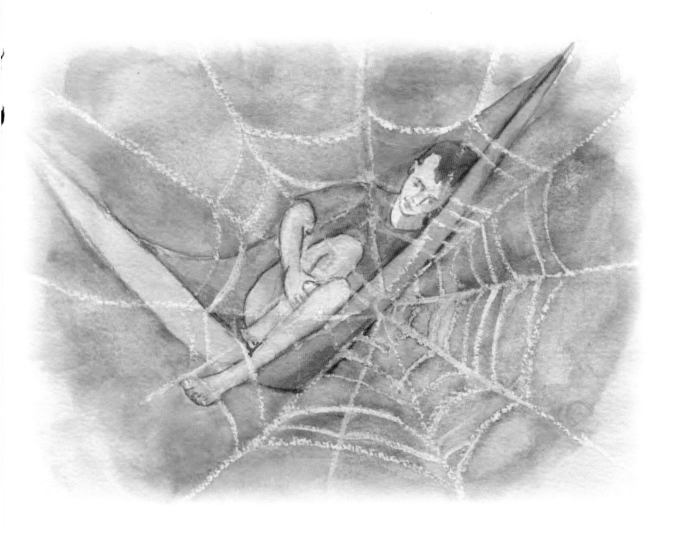

Yahweh

Father

Brahman

Mother

Lord

Allah

God

Almighty

Creator

Saviour

GreatSpirit

Jehovah